"What Am I?"

A Collection of Traditional Word Riddles

DELUXE EDITION
including the complete and refreshed Volume One and Two

Zack Guido

www.wildguess.co

ISBN-13: 978-1950601004
ISBN-10: 1950601005

for CM

TABLE OF CONTENTS

INTRODUCTION

This book is a collection of traditional-style word riddles. Its purpose is to entertain and stimulate your mind by mixing the classic child-like form with some modern twists. By the end of it, you might not see everyday things in the same way.

These riddles have some simple rules:

• They have *one* intended answer. Some may *seem* to have multiple solutions, and you may discover new, unintended answers, but they were written with one specific solution in mind.

• Each line is important and the answer must satisfy all given clues.

• Some of the clues and solutions may include homonyms, which I hope add fun wordplay and an additional level of challenge. Keep this in mind as you work out the riddles!

The solutions are located on the back of each page, directly behind each riddle. They are intentionally hard to read, in order to help avoid the accidental spoiling of answers you didn't want to see. Don't look unless you absolutely have to!

HOMONYMS, HOMOPHONES, HOMOGRAPHS, HETERONYMS, HETEROGRAPHS

Homonyms, homophones, homographs, heteronyms, and heterographs are linguistic terms that describe sets of words that share a spelling and/or pronunciation but have individual meanings. In the whirled of wordplay, they are sum of the mane peaces in uh righter's toolkit.

A handful of riddles in this book include some of these 'tricks', so here's a quick primer:

Homonyms are words with different meanings that share the same spelling and pronunciation – such as SET, which has over four-hundred unique definitions in the Oxford English Dictionary.

Homophones are words with different meanings that share the same pronunciation and may or may not share the same spelling – such as FLOUR & FLOWER, KERNAL & COLONEL, and FAIR & FAIR.

Homographs are words with different meanings that share the same spelling and may or may not share the same pronunciation – such as BOW & BOW and LIE & LIE. If they share the same pronunciation, they are also homonyms; if they don't share the same pronunciation, they are also heteronyms.

Heteronyms, as just explained, are words with different meanings that share the same spelling but have a different pronunciation – such as LEAD & LEAD, which when pronounced one way is a metal and when pronounced another way can mean "to be in charge of."

Heterographs are words with different meanings that share the same pronunciation but have a different spelling – such as the previous example, FLOUR & FLOWER.

Some of these terms overlap similarly to quadrilaterals, rectangles, and squares. The table below may help clear things up:

	Same Meaning?	Same Spelling?	Same Pronunciation?
Homonym	no	yes	yes
Homophone	no	—	yes
Homograph	no	yes	—
Heteronym	no	yes	no
Heterograph	no	no	yes

A famous and grammatically correct sentence demonstrating complications and absurdity that can come from homonyms is:

Buffalo buffalo Buffalo buffalo buffalo buffalo Buffalo buffalo.

This sentence uses three different meanings of the word BUFFALO: the city of Buffalo, NY; the plural form of "buffalo" the animal; and the verb "buffalo" which means "to intimidate."

The sentence is made clearer when rewritten as:

> *Some buffaloes from Buffalo that other buffaloes from Buffalo*
> *buffalo in turn buffalo other buffaloes from Buffalo.*

And it is made clearest when rewritten without the word BUFFALO at all:

> *New York bison that other New York bison bully go on to bully*
> *even more New York bison.*

Finally, here are two examples of using homonyms to have fun:

A joke as old as time:

Why was six afraid of seven?

And a riddle:

You have lost your keys and are distraught. Your friend, a fan of
homophones, says just four words that not only comfort and con-
sole you, but also provide the location of your lost keys. All four
words are homophones of each other. What are they?

(answers are on the next page, directly behind the joke and riddle)

Because seven ate nine.

"There there, they're there."

FAMOUS RIDDLES

The Riddle of the Sphinx

In the ancient Greek story of Oedipus, a Sphinx guarding the road from Delphi to Thebes prevents anyone from leaving or entering their city. The Sphinx asks a challenging riddle that must be answered correctly to continue down the road – getting it wrong gets you killed! Oedipus figures out the correct answer and the Sphinx throws herself off a cliff, freeing the people of Thebes. The Sphinx's riddle is the most famous of all time:

What walks on four feet in the morning,
Two in the afternoon,
And three at night?

Harry Potter Meets A Sphinx

In J.K. Rowling's fourth Harry Potter book, *Harry Potter and the Goblet of Fire*, Harry crosses paths with a sphinx in a maze. The sphinx challenges him to a riddle that he must answer correctly in order to pass, as an homage to the story of Oedipus:

First think of the person who lives in disguise,
Who deals in secrets and tells naught but lies.
Next tell me what's always the last thing to mend,
The middle of middle and end of the end.
And finally give me the sound often heard,
During the search for a hard-to-find word.
Now string them together, and answer me this,
Which creature would you be unwilling to kiss?

Man
(who crawls on all fours as a child,
walks on two legs as an adult,
and walks with a third leg, a cane, as an old man)

Spider
("Spy" + "D" + "Er")

The Impossible Puzzles of The Hobbit

In J.R.R. Tolkein's classic, *The Hobbit*, there are ten famously difficult (some arguably unfair) riddles. They are provided here without context as to not spoil anything from the story:

What has roots as nobody sees,
Is taller than trees,
Up, up it goes,
And yet never grows?

Thirty white horses on a red hill,
First they champ,
Then they stamp,
Then they stand still.

Voiceless it cries,
Wingless flutters,
Toothless bites,
Mouthless mutters.

Mountain

Teeth

Wind

An eye in a blue face
Saw an eye in a green face.
"That eye is like to this eye"
Said the first eye,
"But in low place, not in high place."

It cannot be seen, cannot be felt,
Cannot be heard, cannot be smelt.
It lies behind stars and under hills,
And empty holes it fills.
It comes first and follows after,
Ends life, kills laughter.

A box without hinges, key, or lid,
Yet golden treasure inside is hid.

"Sun on the daisies."
(Very difficult. Some would say too difficult!)

Dark
(Darkness)

Egg

Alive without breath,
As cold as death;
Never thirsty, ever drinking,
All in mail never clinking.

No-legs lay on one leg,
Two-legs sat near on three-legs,
Four-legs got some.

This thing all things devours;
Birds, beasts, trees, flowers;
Gnaws iron, bites steel;
Grinds hard stones to meal;
Slays king, ruins town,
And beats high mountain down.

Fish

"Fish on a little table, man at table sitting on a stool, the cat has the bones."
(Yes, that is the answer.)

Time

The Unsolvable Riddle

Alice's Adventures in Wonderland, the classic 1865 fantasy novel by master puzzler Lewis Carroll (known by his mother as Charles Lutwidge Dodgson), is famous for its wit and wordplay. At the Mad Hatter's tea party, many people's favorite scene, Alice is asked this now-famous riddle:

Why is a raven like a writing desk?

"I haven't the slightest idea."

That is the answer given to Alice by the Mad Hatter when she asks him for the solution.

Lewis Carroll's intention was that this riddle have no real answer, though after receiving many letters from readers who were curious about the riddle he provided some possible answers in the preface of a future edition of the book:

> "Enquiries have been so often addressed to me, as to whether any answer to the Hatter's Riddle can be imagined, that I may as well put on the record here what seems to me to be a fairly appropriate answer: 'Because it can produce a few notes, though they are very flat; and it is nevar put with the wrong end in front!' This however, is merely an afterthought; the riddle as originally invented has no answer at all."

Notice the intentional misspelling of "never" as "nevar", which is "raven" put with its wrong end in front (spelled backwards). Never a dull moment with Lewis Carroll.

ORIGINAL RIDDLES

One way I'm loose, one way I'm tight;
Out with left, in with right.
What am I?

My full power comes when my makers are dead;
I await a heavy hat that goes on my head.
What am I?

The more of me you take,
The more of me there are;
I'm few when gone a little,
But many when gone afar.
What am I?

Screw / Screwdriver

Prince / Princess

Footsteps

Three holes to hold me;
Some strength to throw me;
To do well at my job, you need to control me;
You throw me away, I always come back;
I come in all colors, but traditionally I'm black.
What am I?

Growing one at a time in the dark, shining in the light;
The paler that I am, the more that I am liked;
My maker never gets paid, but never goes on strike.
What am I?

Thursday before Tuesday;
Three before two;
Today before yesterday;
Me before you.
What am I?

Bowling Ball

Pearl

Dictionary

I have two bodies joined as one;
Watch this trick:
I'll flip, stand still, and run.
What am I?

I can be caught, but I can't be thrown;
I'm harder to catch if you're always alone.
What am I?

On my feet I am a shield,
On my head I am a cup;
When things stay up I stay down,
When they come down I go up.
What am I?

Hourglass

A Cold

Umbrella

A sentry in the dark;
I firmly stand my ground;
The longer I stand up,
The shorter I sit down.
What am I?

I can run but I can't walk;
I make noise but I don't talk;
I move what moves me;
Constantly thirsty.
What am I?

I take you to the nines, and to thirteen too;
I love, shine, beat, dig,
And go with or into shoes.
What am I?

Candle

Automobile Engine

Suit (clothing or playing cards)

I help to make you comfortable,
I must work while you're awake;
When you're asleep I do my job,
Not taking a single break;
Partly a guard, partly a case;
Not hard to move, but always in the same place.
What am I?

You always have me with you,
You always leave me behind;
But if you go and break the rules,
Then with tools someone may try to find.
What am I?

I'm the beginning of every instant,
The end of a quick hello;
When I'm alone I stand tall on my own;
I come in at nine, and at fifty-three;
You need me, you bleed me, what is I really...
What am I?

Eyelid

Fingerprints

The Letter I, Iodine

I can taste good when fake, I dangle in lakes;
I may come in an unreal can;
Misspell my name and I'll blow a flame;
And with a book I become a man.
What am I?

I start out surrounded by rock;
They find me, they free me, and then they between me,
In wood with some rubber on top.
What am I?

Brothers and sisters I have seven,
But really I used to have eight;
As the biggest they stare from way over there,
But they're shocked when they find out my weight.
What am I?

Worm

Lead / Graphite

Jupiter

Right-side-up I am who I am,
Upside-down I may stay the same;
I move up and down slightly,
I'm scissored quite nicely,
And I'm short for a twice-as-long name.
What am I?

Easy to look at, impossible to see;
An eight's an eight,
A three's an E,
And an E's a three to me.
What am I?

I can be a coat, but only when I'm wet;
People may say they'd like to watch me do what I do,
Rather than doing what you suggest.
What am I?

BOB

Mirror

Paint

Confined in a tube,
Warmer or cooler I move;
If you try to freeze me,
It sure won't be easy,
And whatever you do, don't ever free me!
What am I?

You can call me but I don't have a phone;
I may be in your apartment, but probably not in your home;
I go through the ceiling; I go through the floor;
I don't have a handle, I do have a door.
What am I?

I use four of mine,
To rest two of yours;
Pulled out, pushed in,
But not so much at church.
What am I?

Mercury

Elevator

Chair

Zero has none,
The same as one;
Two has three,
The same as four;
But two have more.
What am I?

When first comes in second,
And second comes in first,
And first and second did the best,
But also did the worst.
What am I?

I'm made out of five letters,
I'm made out of seven letters;
I have keys, but I don't have locks;
I'm concerned with time, but not with clocks.
What am I?

Telephone Keypad

A Tie

Music / Piano

We come as five,
Sometimes six;
Rarely ever do we all hang together,
But with the rest of our friends,
We make a nice mix.
What am I?

I don't need shoes,
I don't have feet;
I can't cook a thing,
But need heat to find something to eat.
What am I?

People love when they see me,
I appear strictly and routinely;
I typically stay in the sky,
But can't float, move, or fly.
What am I?

Vowels

Snake

Rainbow

I will tell you what you want to know,
But only under pressure;
You stand up tall to ask me your question,
But can rarely stand my answer.
What am I?

You can hook me but I'm not a fish;
You can drive me but I have no wheels;
You can slice me but I stay in one piece.
What am I?

I only fall when big enough,
And only rise when small;
You feel me when I'm falling down,
But on my way back up you can't feel me hardly at all.
What am I?

Scale

Golf Ball

Raindrop / Water

I roam the Earth with four big legs,
And with a tiny tail;
My home can also be on a spoon,
And even in your hair.
What am I?

You can find me in a pond,
But I cannot get wet;
If you're a blonde then I'm a blonde,
And if not, I'm probably a brunette.
What am I?

When I'm standing first in line,
I matter not at all;
But switch my place and you will find,
That line is not as small.
What am I?

Moose / Mousse

Reflection

Zero

One of us can cause a riot, two can keep the peace;
We're similar in many ways but individually unique;
One can show you truly care,
One can show you truly swear,
And one can tell you bad or good;
You can't misplace us but we can be lost,
Though it's okay, you'll have a spare.
What am I?

You have to give me to someone in order to keep me.
What am I?

I used to be important to you,
Now, not so much;
Take me out next week sometime,
Either after dinner, or way before lunch.
What am I?

Fingers

Your Word

Garbage

Some people point me,
Noble people take me,
Some people pass me,
And I'm a game some insist on playing.
What am I?

I can be drawn but still be nothing,
I can be shot but still be nothing;
And the best way to take me away,
Is to fill me in with something.
What am I?

We're five little girls and we all look alike,
But we're equally different in our widths and our heights;
We live with each other and each have our own space,
But we all stand together in the exact same place;
We're usually happy, but can't change the look on our face.
What are we?

Blame

Blank

Matryoshka (Russian) Dolls

You can take your stick and hit me,
But you can't hit my friends;
That's my job and mine alone,
Don't scratch me at the end.
What am I?

The royal couple and their court,
Having good old-fashioned fun;
Some matter more and some matter less,
But any one can get the job done.
What am I?

One comes before the other,
The other comes before the one;
Like the chicken and its egg,
No one knows which one begun.
Certain people have a certain preference,
For during which they get their work done.
What am I?

Cue Ball

Chess Pieces

Day and Night

At night you tell me what to do,
At morning I do what I'm told;
As I steadily come closer to doing my job,
You're steadily getting old.
What am I?

I stand straight up, I'm hard to move,
Buried in the ground, I'm etched and grooved;
Once I'm yours, I'm yours to keep,
Once you get me, others might weep.
What am I?

I stand there blushing beside the road;
I give legal advice, so do what you're told;
Technically speaking, you must do it completely.
What am I?

Alarm Clock

Tombstone

Stop Sign

I stay in place, guarding a space;
Many people hate me and get right in my face;
They tend to stay for an hour or two,
Pay me or I'll tell on you.
What am I?

To use me you dip me,
Some leave me, some jig me;
I work from a bag unless you are fancy;
Use me too much and you might get antsy.
What am I?

I talk a lot at work, but never say what's on my mind;
I listen too, and wait for my cue;
To say and hear the same thing many, many times.
What am I?

Parking Meter

Tea Bag

Actor

I don't have a color, but I can be white;
I'm not a magician, but I am a type of sleight;
I can cause pain, I can relieve;
I do my job best when people believe.
What am I?

I can be breaking, but cannot be broken;
I'm after-the-fact, I'm written and spoken;
I can be good, bad, or neutral,
Really that's up to you;
My goal is to be black and white,
But I can take on a yellowish hue.
What am I?

I have many keys, but only some are used for locking;
My partner does the moving, I do the talking.
What am I?

Lie

News

Computer Keyboard

You, just you, can walk with me,
But I will have to run;
Where we are when we begin,
Is where we are when we are done.
What am I?

People tend to lose me,
When things do not go right;
No one sees me until I'm lost,
I'm known to start a fight.
What am I?

I come by the dozen,
And by thirty too;
Sometimes even thirty-one,
But never thirty-two.
What am I?

Treadmill

Temper

Month

I'm known to be quick, but not known to be noticed;
I happen less often the more that you focus;
When I happen it's two things at once,
Thousands of times a day,
Every day, every month.
What am I?

I can wave, but I can't wave goodbye;
I act like a clock, but don't tell the time;
I hang, I stand, I swivel, I sit;
I can do what a mouth does, but can't swallow or spit.
What am I?

If I'm long, I might be heavy,
I'm just one thing, but made of many;
A whole made out of holes;
Sometimes I keep two things together,
Sometimes I just hang out and pose.
What am I?

Blink

Fan

Chain

Nobody wants to eat me, but they all end up taking a bite;
It's not that I am tempting, but I'm a fate that they can't fight;
I sit on your shelf, but I'm not a book;
I'm in your kitchen cabinets, but not used to cook;
I'm in your bedroom too, and your closet, and your den;
And week after week you get rid of me,
But I always come back again.
What am I?

I'm put on a horse, but not on its back;
And not on its feet, I don't leave a track;
Not in its hair, not on its face, I'm not placed for style;
And usually I don't last long, just for a little while.
What am I?

I'm a type of language, but I'm not meant for speaking;
You will find me everywhere, but people rarely read me;
I'm simple to write, and simple to understand,
But to translate a book into me would take years to do by hand.
What am I?

Dust

Bet / Wager

Binary

The lowest number's rank;
The highest rank of any;
I'm famously known as a crown that sank,
And I'm sought after by many.
What am I?

I can't stand up unless I'm moving,
And I move fast, but don't move much;
As I move it's physics I'm proving;
Don't interrupt me, please, don't touch.
What am I?

Sometimes bought, sometimes sold,
Sometimes kept, sometimes told;
Most potent when least expected;
Making careers out of being intercepted.
What am I?

Gold

Spinning Top

Secret

I'm something very common, you see me all around;
I live on the water, in the air, and on the ground;
But there's something not so common about me:
When I grow up, I grow down.
What am I?

I'm how something might go by,
I'm what something might go through,
I'm something that a someone,
Might accidentally pass to you.
What am I?

I can hold a mountain up,
And keep down a whole sea;
The closer you get, the further I stay,
You can run, run, run but you can't catch up to me.
What am I?

Goose / Duck

Flew / Flue / Flu

Horizon

Stiff little people on a field, standing in a row;
Though they're stiff, they're nimble and swift,
They kick, they slide, they move side to side,
And round and round they go.
What am I?

When you sit down you have me,
When you stand I'm gone;
Sit again, I come right back,
Because I've been there all along.
What am I?

A taxicab for one,
That starts when you are done;
It's a one-way trip that doesn't go quick,
And the tip I get? None.
What am I?

Foosball Table

Lap

Hearse

I'm always on my way, steadily getting closer;
But just as soon as I arrive,
I have to start all over.
What am I?

I come in different lengths, different sizes, similar shapes;
I need to be maintained, I can be painted, I can be fake;
I typically come as twenty, in four sets of five,
I chip, I crack, I break, I snap,
But I come back every time.
What am I?

Every year on my birthday, I get myself a ring;
But I never have room for another,
That is, until I get the freaking thing.
What am I?

Tomorrow

Nails

Tree

I am a food with three letters in my name;
Leave just the first and I still sound the same.
What am I?

Individually we're each unique,
Together we look sleek;
Against triplets we win,
Against four, try again;
We share more than just color,
We belong with one another.
What am I?

Something makes me,
Then you take me,
Then you break me,
Then remake me.
What am I?

Pea

A Flush in a Poker Game

Egg

The harder you try to catch something else,
The harder it is to catch me.
What am I?

Nobody really reads me,
Nobody really needs me;
It takes two different types of skill,
To write me and to remove me.
What am I?

I'm a little bit of money,
I've made famous the rose,
I'm what you've done when you've delivered,
I'm each and all of those.
What am I?

Your Breath

Appendix

Cent / Scent / Sent

I can't go from here to there,
But I can go from there to here;
And what I mean by "go", is that I disappear.
What am I?

You will find a little bit of me in a library,
A place I'm not supposed to be around;
People question my presence when lonely trees fall down.
What am I?

Half of my name is stupid,
Half of my name is loud;
If you use me regularly,
You will soon be proud.
What am I?

The Letter "T"

Sound

Dumbbell

I have no wings, yet I do fly;
I have no eyes, yet I do cry;
Sometimes low, but always high;
If I get too heavy, I'll drop by.
What am I?

Insatiable appetite, and at times I have a temper;
I don't like to swim, and sometimes I mind the weather;
I'm not goods with books, I can set the mood;
I am not a cook, but I can make you food.
What am I?

They make me from a recipe,
Dry, then wet, then dry again;
But whatever you do, don't eat me,
Or you might not eat again;
And when I go from place to place,
They take me for a spin.
What am I?

Cloud

Fire

Concrete

You pick me out and pick me up,
Then you pull me down;
Then later on you pull me up,
And throw me in a basket or on the ground.
What am I?

No hands, two hands, three hands;
Numbers, letters, lines;
Different shapes and sizes,
Showing what's on my mind.
What am I?

They fill me up and you empty me, almost every day;
But if you twist my arm, I'll work the opposite way.
What am I?

Shirt

Clock

Mailbox

You're in me and outside me;
You guide me but don't ride me;
I can have a tongue, but I can't have a mouth;
Sometimes headed north, always stationed south.
What am I?

I'm made of eight letters,
And can hold a ninth inside;
Pay a small amount,
Send me for a ride.
What am I?

I always run, I never walk;
I have a mouth, I never talk;
I have a bed, I never sleep;
I can be shallow, I can be deep.
What am I?

Shoes

Envelope

.

River

I can come in a can;
I can come as a punch;
I can come as a win;
You can eat me for lunch.
What am I?

First I am planted, watered, and reapt,
Then I am dried, and then I am wet;
The longer I swim, the more taste you get.
What am I?

I can be pretty, sleepy, or dreamy,
And I come in different shades;
I'm always moving around but always in the same place,
And you use me every day.
What am I?

Beet / Beat

Coffee

Eyes

You buy me taken apart,
To redo what's been undone;
Four of my parts have one big corner,
The rest of them have none.
What am I?

Everyone has me,
Everyone needs me;
But I can make people sick to their stomachs,
Even if they only see me.
What am I?

I'm scared of the water,
But not scared of heights;
I come many in a box, and the box will be light,
The box might be colored, but I will be white.
What am I?

Jigsaw Puzzle

Blood

Tissue

I fly without feathers;
Sleep while you're awake;
I'm not a mosquito and neither a needle,
But blood I am known to take.
What am I?

I can't move on my own,
But I'm known for my rolling;
With money and a lot of luck,
You might get rich quick when you throw me.
What am I?

You can use me to stop,
You can take me to smoke;
Not only do I stop, but I am a stop,
And the result of a stick's first stroke.
What am I?

Vampire Bat

Dice

Brake / Break

Sometimes I move fast,
Sometimes I move slow;
Truly my speed is constant,
Yet nowhere do I go.
What am I?

I'm right under your nose,
I'm always on your mind;
A certain type of case,
An archaeologist's find.
What am I?

We always come together,
But one of us comes first;
And before we finally do arrive,
You'll look like you could burst.
What am I?

Time

Skull

Twins

Clean when black,
Dirty when white;
Get too close,
Sneeze you might.
What am I?

You have me today,
Tomorrow you'll have more;
As time passes,
I'm not as easy to store;
I don't take up much space,
And in one place I'll be;
I am what you saw,
But not what you see.
What am I?

I'm essential to most flight,
But can't fly on my own;
I move the air to make the lift,
But I'm not made, I'm grown.
What am I?

Chalkboard

Memories

Feathers

Very few men have ever been here,
But one's stayed for thousands of years.
You can see him many days per month,
As long as conditions are clear.
What am I?

I build crowns not for queens,
And bridges not for feet;
I like to keep things nice and clean,
My friends keep things straight and neat.
What am I?

I'm rough to the touch;
I'm done through veins;
I'm taken in math;
I'm the path of a plane.
What am I?

The Moon

Dentist

Coarse / Course

You can't see me,
But I see you;
To be more specific,
I see through.
What am I?

I like to roam but I always stay home,
Leaving a track while I trek;
If you moved like I move and carried what I carry,
You'd break your back and your neck.
What am I?

I can be thin but I can't be fat,
And you need me to be around you;
Not only can I not suffocate you,
But I can't even crowd you.
What am I?

X-ray

Snail

Air

I have lakes but no water,
No cars, but I have streets;
Many places, many borders,
But I am all in one piece.
What am I?

I'm always hungry, I'll always eat;
Fill my mouth and turn to feed me,
I keep my food pointy and neat.
What am I?

When people add me they're often shaking;
On the tips of tongues there's no mistaking;
I'm there to help when the devil is waiting.
What am I?

Map

Pencil Sharpener

Salt

I have three feet but I can't walk;
I tell you things but I can't talk;
Sometimes I swivel, but most times I'm straight;
I'm like a scale, but can't tell your weight.
What am I?

The things I bite don't bleed,
And I don't bite until you push me;
I bring my victims together with my bite,
But they'll split up if you pull just right.
What am I?

I'm just like a doll, but I'm not for playing;
I stand up very straight, but if windy I may be laying;
I'm pretty well-known, famous for no brain;
I work outside whether sunshine, clouds, or rain.
What am I?

Yardstick

Stapler

Scarecrow

I have teeth, sometimes they're fine;
Up on your head, then down by your spine.
What am I?

Made for one but meant for two;
Worn for years, but usually just a few;
I was made for "me and you";
You won't need me until you say you do.
What am I?

The family I come from is known to be crazy;
I'm good when alone and when spread I'm amazing;
That's not objective, it's a matter of taste;
I'm good for your health, but bad for your waist.
What am I?

—

Comb

Wedding Ring

Peanut

I live where it is dry,
I live where it is wet;
I'm blinding when I'm in your eyes,
But with heat, pressure, and a certain shape,
I have the opposite effect.
What am I?

I'm lighter than what makes me,
You see through me but can't miss me;
When things are awkward you might try to break me,
And I might stick to you if you kiss me.
What am I?

The first few times I come you don't know it,
And then you don't want to miss me;
After many more I lose my allure,
And your best ones? Those are probably history!
What am I?

Sand

Ice

Birthday

I come across as flat,
But there's more to me than my surface;
You climb my mountains from top to bottom,
And from bottom to top you surface.
What am I?

I'm a hunting device used again and again;
I bend a little bit, but way less than my friend;
For many years I was number one,
But I've been replaced by a deadlier, more modern son.
What am I?

I go up, I go down;
I'm the present, I'm the past;
My sole purpose in life is for kids to have a blast.
What am I?

Ocean

Arrow

Seesaw

I cover your body, but I'm not clothes;
The more I'm used, the thinner I grow;
I'm not skin, but I help make it glow.
What am I?

I'm done to boats, to cargo, to loads;
When indoors I'm, in a way, a narrow road.
What am I?

I have pockets but I'm not pants;
I have legs but I can't dance;
I come in four sizes, depending on your room;
I'm soft and fuzzy, but parts of me are smooth.
What am I?

Bar of Soap

Haul / Hall

Pool Table

I'm something kind of like a clock, in a certain way;
By that I mean I tell the time, but only once per day;
Another point of difference too, between a clock and me:
To know the time from me you listen, a clock you have to see;
I'm not a clock, I told you that, I'm also not a bell,
There are differences between those things and me,
They need batteries, motors, ringers; I just need to be.
What am I?

I'm something you'll find all around you;
I can be clear but I can't be seen through;
If I get cut you can glue me shut, but I can do it on my own too.
What am I?

A rock group with four members,
Each of whom's deceased;
People still come to see us,
Even though an album was never released.
What am I?

Rooster

Skin

Mt. Rushmore

I have two arms, but no fingers or hands;
I have two legs, but only use them to stand;
I carry things for you but you must carry me,
Help me up a little bit and I'll make your job easy.
What am I?

The letters of the alphabets, but only just a few;
It's hard to say whether I was invented or just discovered by you;
You don't use me to talk and I don't make sound,
But I go on and on and on — don't worry, just round!
What am I?

Pencil to paper, pen to pad,
Hidden and locked away;
You tell me things that to others,
You daren't, wouldn't say.
What am I?

Wheelbarrow

Mathematical Constants
(π, e, i, etc.)

Diary

You use me for brushing,
For flushing,
For rushing;
So please go in just one at a time,
Or someone might be blushing.
What am I?

You can touch me,
You can break me,
You can win me,
You can ache me.
What am I?

I sound like a color,
But that's the old me;
I sometimes grow near the water,
I'm a form of what you're doing.
What am I?

Bathroom

Heart

Read / Reed

It's easy to see me,
Not easy to atop me,
Clouds hang around me,
People sometimes slide down me.
What am I?

I used to be for hunting,
Now I'm just for fun;
Toss me out and I'll come back,
I end where I begun.
What am I?

The result of a chafing;
I can stir you by shaking;
You may not feel me every time,
But when you do there's no mistaking.
What am I?

Mountain

Boomerang

Earthquake

You can use me to say goodbye,
You can use me to say hello;
You can even plant me, but the ground isn't where I go.
What am I?

I have hundreds of legs, but I don't stand, I just lean;
You make me feel dirty so that you can feel clean.
What am I?

I'm tall and I'm twisted;
I'm narrow and fast;
I'm there for a moment,
But my devastation lasts.
What am I?

Kiss

Broom

Tornado

Done to the chief,
And to the king too;
Liquid turned to stone,
I can hit and hurt you.
What am I?

I come by the billions, but you can probably only name a few;
Whichever one's your favorite is many, many other people's too.
What am I?

I'm done with a hand, just one for all your time;
A motion to make words, but not one to makes lines;
I'm known to be correct, and as a way, in a way;
If someone asks how to get somewhere,
I might be what you say.
What am I?

Hail

Color

Write / Right

I bend, I snap,
I'm used to wrap:
Money, broccoli, and random crap.
What am I?

I'm something that you kind of eat;
I can be spicy, I can be sweet;
As you get older you don't think of me this way,
But I used to be a treat.
What am I?

I'm delicately attached to something,
To attach it to itself;
I'm usually near you as you sleep,
Probably in a drawer,
Probably not on a shelf.
What am I?

Rubber Band

Gum

Button

I get my name from what I am plus what I'm used to do;
Adult train with me, kids play with me,
And I used to be a fixture during recess at school.
What am I?

I'm physical, I'm digital,
Rectangular and stripped;
I'm limited but with great potential,
And get better as I get chipped.
What am I?

If you really think about it,
I'm worth less than what I say;
Every day you take me with you,
Folded and put away.
What am I?

Jump Rope

Credit Card

Dollar Bill

"THE WORLD IS FULL OF OBVIOUS THINGS WHICH NOBODY BY ANY CHANCE EVER OBSERVES."

– Sherlock Holmes

44337566R00083

Made in the USA
Lexington, KY
09 July 2019